MERLIN

Published By Century Books Limted,
Unit I, Upside Station Building, Solsbro Road, Torquay, Devon, TQ2 6FD.
books@centurybooksltd.co.uk
Published 2012.

Merlin created by
Julian Jones, Jake Michie, Julian Murphy and Johnny Capps.

Join Merlin on:
Facebook www.facebook.com/MerlinOfficial

Twitter www.twitter.com/MerlinOfficial

and check out the new official Merlin YouTube channel
www.youtube.com/merlinofficial

CONTENTS

£7.99

MERLIN

When Merlin first arrived in Camelot, his character and his powers were undeveloped and immature. His experiences since then have changed and challenged him, and now he is completely at home in Camelot. For the first time in his life, he feels that he belongs somewhere.

Merlin and Arthur are much more than just master and servant; they are also good friends. Arthur relies on Merlin to give him wise advice. Merlin knows that he has to be strong for Arthur's sake.

Despite their closeness, Merlin cannot reveal to Arthur that he has magical powers, because Arthur still believes in his father's rules banning magic. Merlin dreams of a land where he can be free to be his true self, but he knows that the time is not yet right...

Secret identity: Emrys

ARTHUR

Arthur is caring and kind, but he hasn't always been allowed to show it. Uther brought him up to be a brave warrior and taught him to hide his feelings away. However, he cares deeply about his people, and is developing into a wise and good leader. He always stands by what he believes to be right, and his fairness and honesty are some of his greatest qualities.

Now Arthur has been thrown in at the deep end. He has taken responsibility for the kingdom because Uther has lost his mind, and he knows that there are more important things than his own personal happiness. Camelot always comes first for Arthur – even before his true love, Gwen.

True love: Gwen

GAIUS

Respected Court Physician Gaius looked after Merlin when he first arrived in Camelot. He recognised that Merlin was destined for great things, and since then he has watched over the young warlock as he discovered the secrets of Camelot.

Gaius has some magical abilities himself, although they are not as powerful as Merlin's. But his experience and knowledge are invaluable as Merlin learns his art.

Gaius may seem grumpy and dour, but underneath his crusty manner he has a kind and noble heart. He has been at Uther's side for more than twenty years as his advisor, while also secretly rescuing many people from his dungeons. Gaius is a great friend to Merlin, and is always there to support and defend him – as well as to tell him what he has done wrong!

Ex-fiancée: Alice

THE GREAT DRAGON

Kilgharrah is one of Albion's last and greatest links with the old magic. He can see Merlin's destiny, and when he was imprisoned beneath Camelot he developed a strong relationship with the young wizard.

Kilgharrah was captured during the Great Purge, when Uther tricked the Dragonlords into calling every Dragon in the land to Camelot. When they were in his domain, he had almost all of them killed, together with their Dragonlord masters. Only Kilgharrah survived.

Uther chained the Great Dragon up below Camelot. As time passed, the magical creature grew bitter and angry. When Merlin finally freed him, he was ready to burn Uther's kingdom and destroy it completely. However, Merlin discovered that he had the power of a Dragonlord, and could tame Kilgharrah. The Great Dragon was banished, but he has a debt to Merlin that must be repaid.

Years in captivity: 22

GWEN

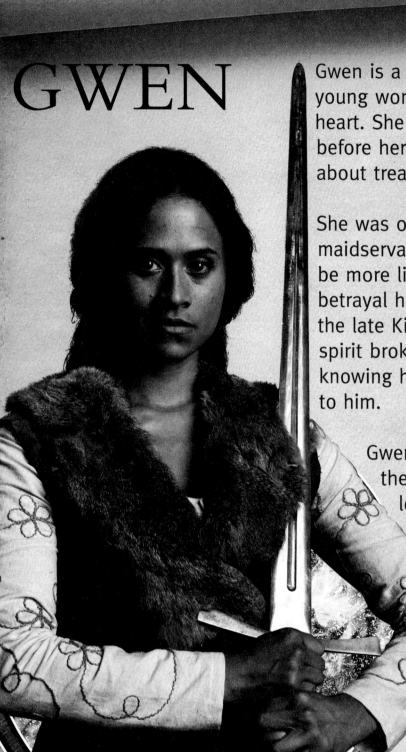

Gwen is a strong, brave and good young woman, with a kind and loving heart. She always thinks of others before herself, and cares passionately about treating people fairly.

She was once Lady Morgana's maidservant although the girls used to be more like best friends. Morgana's betrayal hurt her deeply. She cared for the late King Uther when he had his spirit broken, all for the love of Arthur, knowing how much his father meant to him.

Gwen and Arthur had to keep their relationship a secret for a long time because it would go against Uther's beliefs. Gwen's days of being awkward and shy are gone. She feels able to stand up for what she believes in, even if her actions put her in danger.

Finally Gwen has become the Queen she was always destined to be, a queen for the people and Arthur's one true love.

Parents' jobs: Blacksmith and maid

MORGANA

As the King's daughter, Morgana was once close friends with Merlin and at home in Camelot. She was kind and caring, but her magical powers of foresight frightened her. Gradually, Uther's hatred of magic turned her against him. She discovered that she had a half-sister, Morgause, and eventually she became twisted and corrupted to Morgause's evil ways. In the war against magic, she chose the side of the Old Religion.

Morgana has grown in power and confidence. She has great focus and determination, especially now that her sister Morgause is dead. She wants to overthrow Camelot and seize the throne, because only then will she feel that she has been accepted for who she truly is. Her family has turned on her, so she is determined to have her revenge.

Arthur is the only person who stands in Morgana's way. Hungry for power, and ruthless in her ambition to control Camelot, she will do everything possible to destroy him.

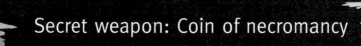

Secret weapon: Coin of necromancy

UTHER

King Uther was a tyrant who hated magic with a passion. He blamed it for the loss of his wife Ygraine. They used magic to help them to have a child, but the price was Ygraine's death.

In grief and anger, Uther slaughtered the Dragons and had all practitioners of magic killed. However, he was blind to the magical powers of his own daughter, and he turned her against him through his merciless war on magic.

Uther wanted Arthur to be the best king that had ever lived. He may have been a cruel king in many ways, but he was capable of great love and strong passions. It was his deep love that led to the Great Purge, and he passed his capacity for love and hate to his children.

Uther met his end at the hands of the Gleeman, a formidable enemy that infiltrated Camelot.

Most famous for: The Great Purge

AGRAVAINE

Lord Agravaine is the brother of Arthur's mother, Ygraine. He is next in line to the throne after his nephew, and pretends to care about Arthur. However, he is a liar and a traitor.

As Arthur's uncle, Agravaine should be doing everything possible to protect him, but his loyalties lie elsewhere. Arthur's birth caused his much-loved sister's death, and he wants to help Morgana to seize the throne.

Agravaine is charming and persuasive, and Arthur believes in him completely. With his father unable to rule the kingdom, the prince relies on his uncle to advise him well – even when Agravaine encourages him to go against his own instincts.

Agravaine is in a good position to exploit his nephew's weaknesses, and he intends to make the most of it. Arthur's life has never been in such grave danger.

Motivation: Revenge

THE KNIGHTS OF THE ROUND TABLE

The Knights of the Round Table are a band of brothers who have formed a strong bond through their shared adventures. The Round Table is all about equality, friendship and helping each other. When the knights sit at the table, no one is in charge – they are all equal. Thanks to them, Camelot is entering a golden age that will never be forgotten.

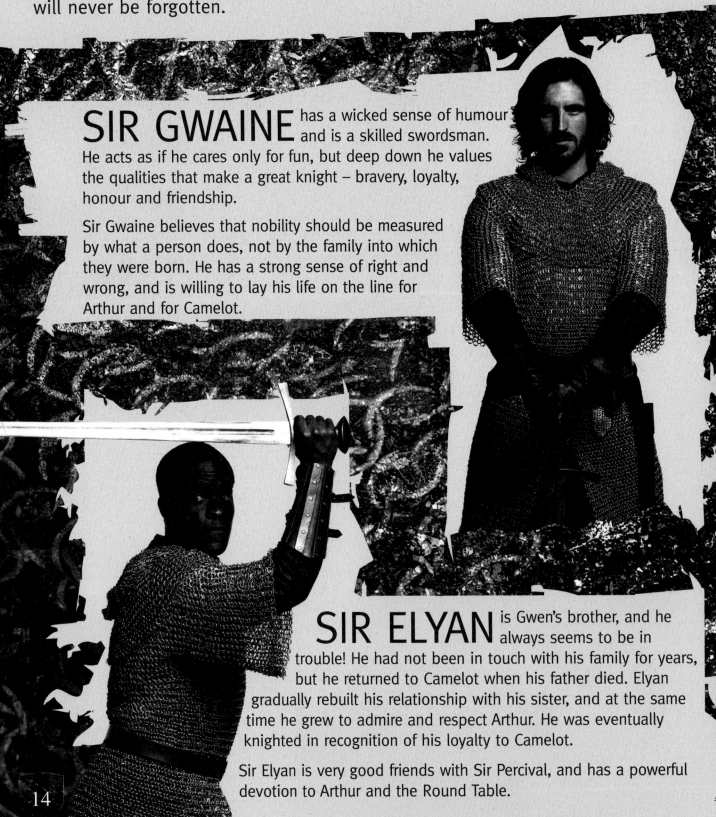

SIR GWAINE
has a wicked sense of humour and is a skilled swordsman. He acts as if he cares only for fun, but deep down he values the qualities that make a great knight – bravery, loyalty, honour and friendship.

Sir Gwaine believes that nobility should be measured by what a person does, not by the family into which they were born. He has a strong sense of right and wrong, and is willing to lay his life on the line for Arthur and for Camelot.

SIR ELYAN
is Gwen's brother, and he always seems to be in trouble! He had not been in touch with his family for years, but he returned to Camelot when his father died. Elyan gradually rebuilt his relationship with his sister, and at the same time he grew to admire and respect Arthur. He was eventually knighted in recognition of his loyalty to Camelot.

Sir Elyan is very good friends with Sir Percival, and has a powerful devotion to Arthur and the Round Table.

SIR PERCIVAL

SIR PERCIVAL is a gentle giant who has great love for Camelot. He is as much admired for his kindness as he is for his strength, and he has a rich sense of humour.

Sir Percival is a friend of Lancelot, which is how he first came to Camelot. Although he is not of noble birth, Arthur knighted him in recognition of his bravery.

SIR LANCELOT

SIR LANCELOT dreamed of becoming a knight of Camelot and is one of the most skilful and loyal of Arthur's knights. He knows Merlin's secret, but he has vowed never to reveal it. Sir Lancelot is a man of honour, and his word can always be trusted.

SIR LEON

SIR LEON is trustworthy and reliable, and has become Arthur's right-hand man. His bravery and steadfastness are invaluable to Arthur, and he has survived several brushes with death.

15

THE STORY SO FAR...

The Kingdom of Camelot is a place of adventure, secrecy and possibility. For years, under the tyrannical rule of King Uther, it has been full of treachery, with villains lurking around every corner. However, King Arthur is determined to make his beloved realm a place of honour and bravery once again.

King Uther tried to destroy all magic in the Great Purge, driving sorcerers into hiding or retirement. The time is still not right for Uther's laws to be overturned, but Arthur has brought new hope to those who believe in the old ways.

When Merlin first arrived in Camelot he had to keep the fact that he was a wizard secret. Only his guardian Gaius knew his secret. He met the Great Dragon and learned that his destiny was to protect Prince Arthur.

Although Arthur still knows nothing of Merlin's magical powers, he now relies on him for friendship, support and advice. Together they face assassins, monsters and sorcerers, and Merlin must help to defeat them all without giving away his great secret.

Unfortunately they hated each other on sight! As time passed, however, Merlin and Arthur grew to respect, like and trust each other.

In these early days of Arthur's rule, Merlin is facing a greater challenge than ever before. As Gwen and Arthur's romance grows stronger, Morgana's powers are threatening the future of Camelot.

She has unleashed evil spirits of the underworld, and Merlin's magic is useless against them. He will need all his wit and wisdom to defeat them and protect Arthur. Can Merlin help Arthur to fulfil his destiny?

HIS FATHER'S SON

Not long after Arthur became King, he found himself defending Camelot against a series of mini invasions. His enemies were testing his strength. Was he as powerful a leader as his father Uther had been?

When King Caerleon was captured after a battle, Agravaine told Arthur that he had to send a clear message to his enemies.

"I suggest that we force him to accept a treaty on our terms," Agravaine said. "He must withdraw his men from our land and return our territories to us."
Arthur agreed, but Merlin thought that he was making a mistake.

"You've always shown mercy in battle," he said. "You've never sought to humiliate your enemy in this way. This isn't like you."

As expected, Caerleon refused to sign the treaty.
"Then you will pay with your life," said Agravaine.
Arthur felt uneasy about killing Caerleon, but afterwards, Agravaine persuaded him that he had done the right thing. Merlin tried to get Arthur to talk about it, but Arthur snapped at him and walked away.

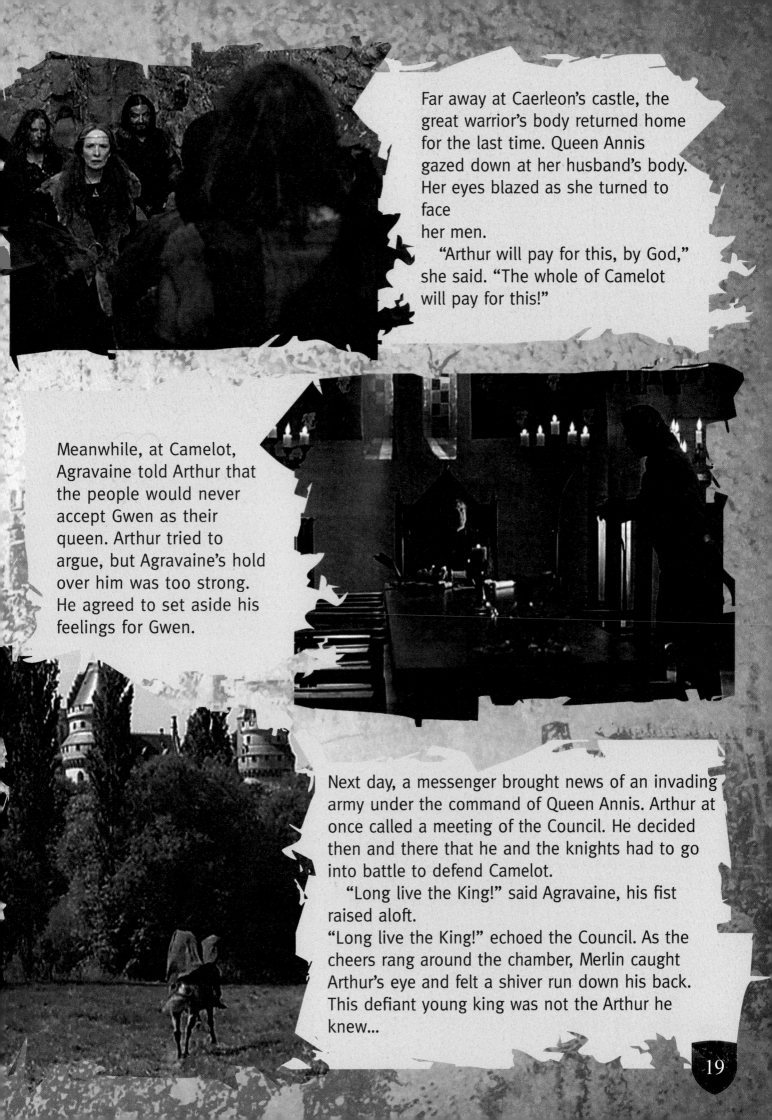

Far away at Caerleon's castle, the great warrior's body returned home for the last time. Queen Annis gazed down at her husband's body. Her eyes blazed as she turned to face
her men.

"Arthur will pay for this, by God," she said. "The whole of Camelot will pay for this!"

Meanwhile, at Camelot, Agravaine told Arthur that the people would never accept Gwen as their queen. Arthur tried to argue, but Agravaine's hold over him was too strong. He agreed to set aside his feelings for Gwen.

Next day, a messenger brought news of an invading army under the command of Queen Annis. Arthur at once called a meeting of the Council. He decided then and there that he and the knights had to go into battle to defend Camelot.

"Long live the King!" said Agravaine, his fist raised aloft.
"Long live the King!" echoed the Council. As the cheers rang around the chamber, Merlin caught Arthur's eye and felt a shiver run down his back. This defiant young king was not the Arthur he knew...

19

That evening, Arthur visited Gwen in her simple home. He felt awkward and uncomfortable, but he knew that he had to be honest with her. He told her that they could not be together because the people would not accept her.

Gwen felt as if her heart might shatter into tiny pieces. She suspected that someone else had put this idea into his head.

"Arthur," she said in a trembling voice, "don't let anyone tell you what to do. You said you are your own man. You have a good heart. Be true to it. Only then will you be the king you want to be."

At Caerleon's castle, the hooded figure of Morgana Pendragon stood before Queen Annis.

"I have come on urgent business," she said.

"What business could you possibly have with me, witch?" Queen Annis demanded.

Morgana explained that she, like Queen Annis, wanted revenge on Arthur.

"If you will accept it, I have come to offer my help," she said.

Next day, Arthur led his knights out of Camelot. He felt the fate of his home and his people resting on his shoulders, and he felt very alone. As the sun set, they saw Queen Annis' army camp. It was a daunting sight.

"Ensure the men have everything they need," he told Agravaine. "They must be well rested by morning. The battle commences at first light."

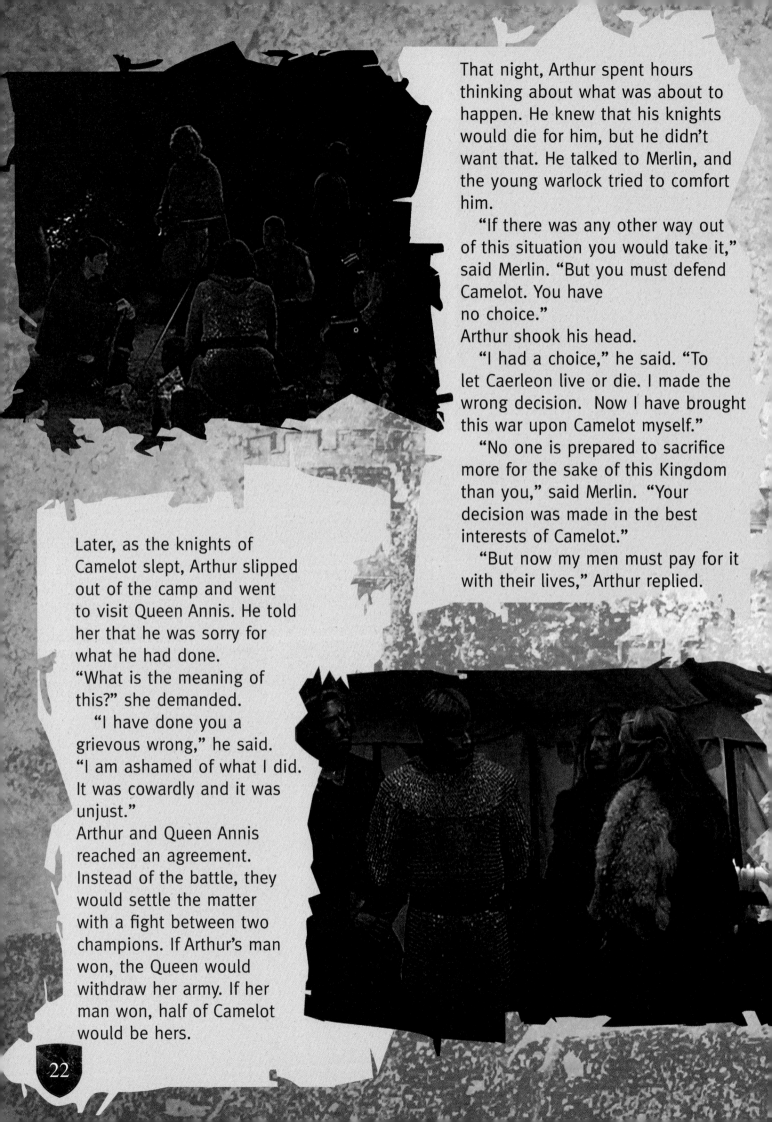

That night, Arthur spent hours thinking about what was about to happen. He knew that his knights would die for him, but he didn't want that. He talked to Merlin, and the young warlock tried to comfort him.

"If there was any other way out of this situation you would take it," said Merlin. "But you must defend Camelot. You have no choice."

Arthur shook his head.

"I had a choice," he said. "To let Caerleon live or die. I made the wrong decision. Now I have brought this war upon Camelot myself."

"No one is prepared to sacrifice more for the sake of this Kingdom than you," said Merlin. "Your decision was made in the best interests of Camelot."

"But now my men must pay for it with their lives," Arthur replied.

Later, as the knights of Camelot slept, Arthur slipped out of the camp and went to visit Queen Annis. He told her that he was sorry for what he had done.
"What is the meaning of this?" she demanded.

"I have done you a grievous wrong," he said. "I am ashamed of what I did. It was cowardly and it was unjust."
Arthur and Queen Annis reached an agreement. Instead of the battle, they would settle the matter with a fight between two champions. If Arthur's man won, the Queen would withdraw her army. If her man won, half of Camelot would be hers.

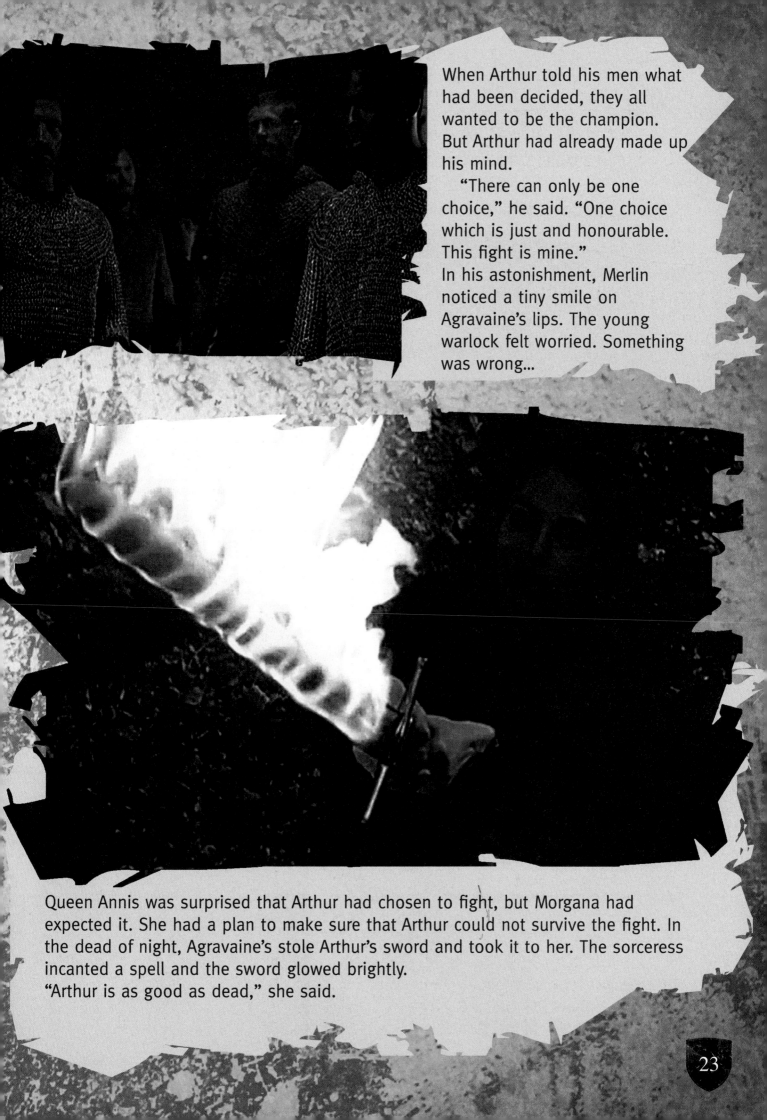

When Arthur told his men what had been decided, they all wanted to be the champion. But Arthur had already made up his mind.

"There can only be one choice," he said. "One choice which is just and honourable. This fight is mine."

In his astonishment, Merlin noticed a tiny smile on Agravaine's lips. The young warlock felt worried. Something was wrong...

Queen Annis was surprised that Arthur had chosen to fight, but Morgana had expected it. She had a plan to make sure that Arthur could not survive the fight. In the dead of night, Agravaine's stole Arthur's sword and took it to her. The sorceress incanted a spell and the sword glowed brightly.

"Arthur is as good as dead," she said.

On the battlefield, Arthur faced Queen Annis' champion – a colossal, savage warrior called Derian. At first the fight seemed fair, pitting Arthur's skill and speed against Derian's size and strength. But then something went wrong. Arthur's sword fell to the ground, dragging his hands down with it. Morgana's magic had made it as heavy as lead, and Derian's blade smashed into Arthur's shoulder as his sword hung heavy in his hand. The King was in terrible danger.

Just in time, Merlin saw Morgana and fought her magic with his own. At last Arthur managed to seize his opponent's sword and overpower him. Everyone expected him to kill Derian, but Arthur spared him.

"It is not victory that I seek, it is peace," said Arthur. "It is my hope that today will mark a new beginning for our kingdoms."

The Queen gave him a curious look.

"There is something about you, Arthur Pendragon," she said. "Something which gives me hope for us all."

Queen Annis told Morgana that she would not help her to take revenge on Arthur.

"I believe I may have misjudged our young King," she said.

"Don't be taken in by his fine words," Morgana snapped.

"It was not Arthur who mislead me, it was you," said the Queen. "You are consumed by bitterness, Morgana. It spreads within you like a disease."

When Arthur returned to Camelot he was met by cheering crowds. But there was one more wrong that he needed to put right . . .

"A good king should do as he sees fit," he told Gwen. "And he should be seen with those he cares for."

Gwen looked into his eyes and felt as if her heart might burst with happiness. The Arthur she knew had returned.

GAIUS'S QUIZ PART ONE

Gaius is looking for a new apprentice. He needs someone with sharp observation skills and a good memory. Test your skills by answering the questions about series two below. You will have to think back a long way to get these questions right!

1. Who tried to take Merlin's job as Arthur's manservant?

2. What is the name of the Great Dragon?

3. Whose handmaiden was Gwen?

4. Who is afraid that she has magic powers?

5. Which knight does Gwen have feelings for?

6. What was Lady Catrina's true identity (which she hid by taking a magic potion)?

7. What was the name of the dreaded witchfinder who suspected Merlin in Episode 7?

8. What did Morgause use to cast a spell on Morgana in Episode 8?

9. What was Freya's secret?

10. What did Trickler use to make Arthur fall in love with Lady Vivian?

Now check your answers and keep a note of your score. You will need it for part two of Gaius's quiz.

CROSSWORD

1. Gaius's job at Camelot is Court ---------
2. Uther's ward
3. Prince (and later King) of Camelot
4. Kilgharrah The Great ------ once imprisoned beneath Camelot
5. Arthur's mother
6. A troll who bewitches Uther
7. The Gleeman is a deadly -------- hiding within Camelot
8. Merlin's job in Camelot
9. Arthur's father
10. The woman Arthur loves

PREDICT THE FUTURE

Great sorcerers have the power to see into the mists of time and predict the future. Now it's your turn! Write your own predictions for 2013 in the boxes below and check back in a year to see if they have come true.

Home

School

Friends

Fun

WORD HUNTER

How many new words can you create from the word

ADVENTURES?

WHO SAID THAT?

Can you identify who said these sentences?
Draw lines to link the words with the correct speakers.

1. I pieced together the Triskelion. I found the path that led us here. The dragon belongs to me. Now hand it over.

2. I made a promise to your mother . . . I'll always be here for you.

3. No pity. No quarter. Do not hesitate for one second. Arthur Pendragon must die.

4. You are destined to be Albion's greatest king. Nothing, not even this stone, can stand in your way. Have faith.

5. Need I remind you the last time you used an ageing spell, you nearly had yourself burnt at the stake.

6. Guinevere made her choice. She betrayed me. Now she must take the consequences.

7. When I was able, I earned my passage the only way I know how – by the sword. Then I slowly made my way north.

8. The Dorocha cannot be allowed to remain in this world. The sundered veil must be restored

Gaius

Morgana

Julius Borden

Merlin

Agravaine

Lancelot

Arther

The Great Dragon

LANCELOT DU LAC

When Arthur tells his uncle that he wants to marry Gwen, Agravaine is far from pleased. "You don't need a woman to support you, sire," he says. "I am your counsel."

"I have made up my mind," says Arthur. "I want Guinevere to be my Queen; and I want you to accept her as such."

Agravaine goes to tell Morgana the news. She is furious.
"I will not see that woman upon my throne," she says. "But there is one person that can ruin King Arthur's plans; one person that can come between them…"

Morgana makes her way to the filthy cave of the Dochraid – an ancient woman who remembers the time of the Old Religion. Morgana needs her help to find out how to use the coin that Morgause gave her.

Morgana travels to the Pool of Nemhain and throws the coin into it. For a few seconds nothing happens. Then a dark figure wades out of the pool and kneels before Morgana. "My name is Lancelot, my Lady. I am yours to command."

Lancelot has returned to life, but he is a shadow of his true self, and only knows that he belongs to Morgana and has to obey her. She is determined to use him to destroy Arthur. She knows that Gwen once had feelings for the handsome knight.

While Morgana is moulding Lancelot's mind to her evil plans, Arthur asks Gwen to marry him. She says yes with tears of happiness in her eyes.

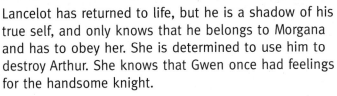

Arthur plans a joust to celebrate their engagement, and Merlin gently teases him about it. Everything seems to be going perfectly, but then a knight arrives riding a white stallion. He presents Gwen with a garland, then removes his helmet. When they see that it is Lancelot, everyone gasps in astonishment.

Lancelot tells them that he was rescued by the Madhavi people. He makes up a story to hide the truth, and almost everyone is delighted. Only Merlin has doubts. He can sense that something is wrong, and he tells Gaius about his fears.
"I want to believe that everything is fine," he tells Gaius. "That we really have Lancelot back."
"What is it?" Gaius asks.
"Something is wrong," says Merlin.

A short time later, Agravaine visits Morgana in the Darkling Woods. He tells her that Arthur and his knights have been completely deceived by Lancelot.
"And Gwen?" Morgana asks. "This must be the last thing she hoped for on the eve of her wedding?"
"I fear she truly does love Arthur," says Agravaine. "Any feelings she had for Lancelot are in the past."

Morgana looks thoughtful, and then takes out a small silver bracelet. She closes her eyes and incants a spell. "Beclypp thinne idese thæt heo hine lyste." A tiny golden flame weaves magically around the bracelet, and then Morgana hands it to Agravaine.

"I think it is time to re-awaken those feelings," she says, with an evil smile.

The following day, Gwen is getting ready for the tournament when Lancelot knocks on her door. He says that he has come to wish her well, and then gives her the bracelet that Morgana has enchanted. "The Madhavi people gave me this token of good fortune for my journey," he says. "I would like you to wear it; for I see their goodness in you. I wish you and Arthur everlasting happiness."

The tournament begins well, and both Arthur and Lancelot win their jousts. Gwen looks on, applauding when Lancelot defeats his opponent.

Meanwhile, Merlin has been looking through ancient books and has guessed the dark magic that Morgana has performed. He asks Gaius if it is possible to raise someone from the dead.
"The old legends do speak of such creatures," says Gaius. "They call them 'Shades'. Poor, tormented souls summoned from their rest by the Necromancer's art."

Later, while Gaius sleeps, Merlin casts a spell. It enables him to see Lancelot as he really is – a terrifying skull and a shadow of his former self.

The next day, Gwen visits Lancelot in his tournament tent. Her feelings have begun to change – she is remembering how it felt to love him.

"I just wanted to wish you well," she says.

"Shouldn't you be saying that to your future husband?" Lancelot asks.

Gwen is flustered.

"I do," she says. "I have. I will."

She leaves, feeling confused and tense, and Lancelot smiles. Morgana's plan is working.

After some nerve-wracking jousts, Arthur and Lancelot face each other in the final. Merlin and Gaius are tense, knowing that Lancelot is not what he seems. Gwen looks excited and nervous.

Arthur and Lancelot charge towards each other. Each rider strikes with sickening force, but they both cling on and turn to face each other again. This time, Arthur is badly hurt. Gwen rises from her chair as the knights charge for a third time. Arthur is unable to protect himself, but at the last moment Lancelot raises his lance and yields – Arthur is safe.

"What's going on?" Merlin wonders in astonishment. "Why did he yield?"

"If Lancelot is not here to kill him, what is he here for?" Gaius asks.

"I don't know," says Merlin. "I wish I did."

That evening, as Lancelot is taking off his armour, Gwen slips into his tent. The bracelet on her wrist glints in the torchlight as their fingers entwine.

Later, Merlin secretly follows Lancelot to the chapel balcony, where he watches the knight meet Agravaine.

"Everything is prepared," says Lancelot. "Gwen is on her way to our assignation as we speak."

"You have done well," says Agravaine. "The Lady Morgana will be very pleased with you."

Merlin follows Lancelot as he makes his way down the corridor. As he nears the end, Merlin reaches out his hand and uses magic to send Lancelot crashing into an arch at the end of the corridor. But Lancelot's foot sweeps Merlin's legs from under him and his sword pommel slams into the back of Merlin's head. Merlin is knocked out.

Agravaine creeps into Arthur's chambers and wakes him.
"There is something you must see, Sire," he says.

Merlin awakes and hurries off down the corridor. Meanwhile, Gwen is meeting Lancelot in the deserted Council Chambers. As they kiss, Arthur enters the room with Agravaine. To his horror, he sees his bride in the arms of his friend.
With a cry of rage, Arthur draws his sword and attacks Lancelot. Merlin whispers a spell to protect Arthur, and Gwen flings herself between the fighting men.
"Stop it!" she cries. "Stop, please – this has to stop. Please!"

Lancelot and Gwen are thrown into cells. Alone, Gwen takes the enchanted bracelet from her wrist and throws it across the room.

Agravaine does everything he can to keep Arthur's anger burning. Merlin hears every word, but can do nothing to stop him.

"In the days of your father, adultery among the noble families was punishable by death," Agravaine says. "And as for Lancelot, death is too good for him. He must die – but painfully."

Merlin can hardly contain his anger, but Arthur remains silent.

In the Council Chambers, Gwen faces the court under guard. She is forced to her knees, but then Arthur asks everyone to leave. He wants to be alone with Gwen.

"What are you still doing on your knees? Am I just your King? Get up, for goodness sake. I was to be your husband."

Angry and sad, Arthur demands an explanation. But Gwen cannot understand what happened to her.

"I was drawn to him," she says. "I couldn't stop myself. I do not know why. I love you. You mean everything to me. All these years I have waited for you."

"You only had to wait one more day," says Arthur.

"All I've ever wanted is to be your Queen," says Gwen. "I still want to be your Queen." Arthur gives a bitter smile. He knows that some people want him to have Gwen executed.

"I don't want to see you dead, Guinevere," he says. "But I don't want to see you. I cannot look on you every day. You will leave Camelot at first light. You return upon pain of death."

"No!" she cries. "I cannot be without you."

Arthur's heart is breaking, but he has made up his mind. Gwen has to leave.

Merlin and Gaius feel terrible. Now they know that this has been Morgana's plan all along.
"It is indeed a cruel revenge," says Gaius.

"If he knew that Lancelot was a Shade..." begins Merlin.

"It wouldn't change what Gwen has done," says Gaius. "It is her betrayal that matters to the King, Merlin. It is Gwen who must pay the price . . ."

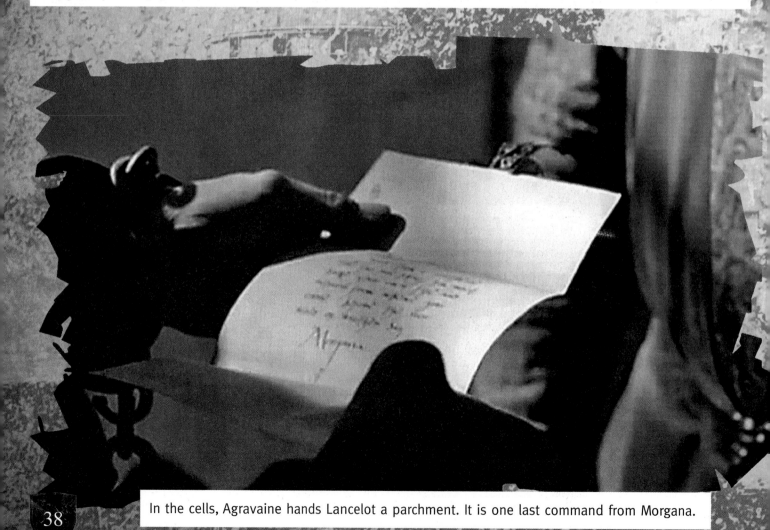

In the cells, Agravaine hands Lancelot a parchment. It is one last command from Morgana.

Arthur watches his servants taking down the decorations for his wedding. Merlin joins him.

"It is not too late, Sire," he says. "I know what Gwen did was desperately wrong; but she is a good person. I truly believe that."

"As do I Merlin," Arthur replies with a sad smile.

"Can you find it in your heart to forgive her?" asks Merlin.

"That is not the problem," says Arthur.

"The people won't think you're weak, or a fool," says Merlin. "They will find you merciful, understanding."

"I love Gwen, with all my heart," says Arthur. "I am sure, in time, I could find a way to forgive her. But I will never trust her. And I cannot live like that; not as a king, and certainly not as a husband. Though it pains me; it is best that she's gone."

Merlin knows that he cannot argue with the King – he has made his decision.

Lancelot takes his own life in the cells of Camelot – Morgana's final command. Merlin gives him a proper burial on the shores of Avalon. The sunlight gleams on the lake as Merlin looks down at the body of his dead friend. He places a hand on his forehead and incants a prayer.

Suddenly, Lancelot's eyes flicker open! He smiles, and Merlin can see that, for this brief moment, he is the Lancelot of old.

"Thank you," he says.

His eyes close again, and his spirit leaves his body. Merlin stands back, his eyes flash, and the pyre bursts into flames. He watches as the boat makes its final journey across the Lake of Avalon, disappearing into the mist...

MAKE A BATTLE SHIELD

You will need:
Large piece of thick card, Sticky tape, Scissors
Glue, Pens , Kitchen foil, Paints and a paintbrush,

Instructions:

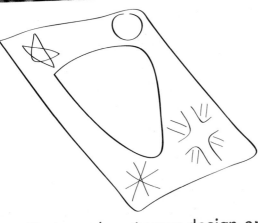

1. First, work out your design on a piece of paper.

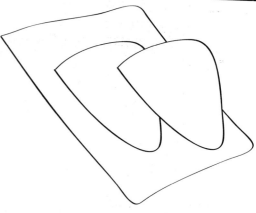

2. Cut the card into the shape of a shield. Use the pictures of Arthur's knights to inspire you!

3. Draw your picture on the front of the shield.

4. Decorate the shield with paint and shapes cut out of foil.

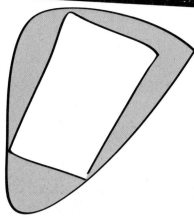

5. Cut a rectangle of card 2 inches shorter than the width of the shield. Tape one end to the shield and then bend the shield to the card, tightly taping the other end to the shield. This will give the shield a curved shape.

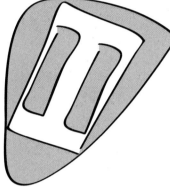

6. Cut two rectangles of card and attach them to the back of your shield with sticky tape to make handles for your arm to pass through.

7. Now you are ready for battle!

WORD SCRAMBLE

Can you see through the confusion? Unscramble the words below and discover the enemies of Camelot.

1. TEH GALEMNE

2. UIUJLS BDEORN

3. AINVAAGRE

4. LAAIM

5. MORNAGA

6. DOCHRAID

7. HET ODCHORA

8. INOD

MERLIN'S MAGIC

Discover some of the incredible spells that Merlin has used, and find out more about them.

Spell: Todæl nu

Phonetic: tow-del noo

Effect: Come apart

Spell: Weor untoworpenlic

Phonetic: Weigh-orth unn-tow-wor-pen-lich

Effect: Become unbreakable

Spell: Forleta me a

Phonetic: Four-let-ath may aah

Effect: Keep away from me

Spell: Geondlihte gesweorce min

Phonetic: Geond-liht-eh yeh-sway-or-che meen

Effect: Light my darkness

Spell: Oferswinge

Phonetic: of-er-swing-eh

Effect: Super punch

Spell: Gehalge

Phonetic: Yeh-hal-yeh

Effect: Restore to health

Spell: ord, wi stand hine

Phonetic: bord, with-stand hin-e

Effect: Move table

Spell: cæga, cum her

Phonetic: cay-yah, coom hair

Effect: Come to me keys

CROSSWORD CHALLENGE

There are no numbers to help you with this crossword. Instead, you have to work out where the answers should go by counting the number of letters in the squares. Are you clever enough to figure out where each answer belongs? Good luck!

Sir Percival is a _____ of Camelot.
Merlin's friend and court physician.
Morgana's former handmaiden.
___ Elyan.
Uther and Arthur's family name.
A knight who loves Gwen.
A powerful sorceress.
The Great dragon.

QUICK WITS

Arthur and Merlin have grown to respect and care for each other, but they still have fun trading insults! Here are some of the best one-liners they have used. Which is your favourite?

A: Don't be such a girl, Merlin.

M: I've told you, you're an ass – I just didn't realise you were a Royal one.

A: You never cease to surprise me. You are a lot smarter than you look.

A: You really are a total buffoon, aren't you?

A: We're supposed to be hunting. It requires speed, stealth and an agile mind.
M: So you're able to get by on two out of three then?

A: Were you born clumsy or do you work at it?

A: Are you deaf?
M: I wish.

M: I'm a terrible liar. I start sweating, my vision blurs, my brain stops working.
A: Well, no change there then.

M: My throat was so dry, I thought I wouldn't be able to talk.
A: Well, at least some good would've come from the drought then.

A: I had no idea you were so keen to die for me.
M: Trust me, I can hardly believe it myself.

A: Do you have any natural gifts, Merlin?
M: No. Let me think . . .
I'm not naturally rude or insensitive . . .
A: Just naturally irritating.

A: I sometimes wonder if you know who I am.
M: Oh, I know who you are.
A: Good.
M: You're a prat.

JOIN CAMELOT!

Become part of the most famous court in Albion! Answer these questions to find your place and identify your position.

You fall over in front of everyone at court and they all laugh. How do you react?
A You feel embarrassed and hide away in your chambers.
B You laugh along with them.
C You say nothing, but you start planning revenge on them all.

How important are the ancient laws of the land?
A Very important – they keep our society as we want it to be.
B Some are important but some are out of date and should be changed.
C I don't care about the law – I do what is right for me.

Do you have any enemies?
A I have argued with one or two people.
B Not that I know of!
C Yes.

Do you have plans for the future?
A Yes, I know exactly what I want to have achieved in five years' time.
B No, I like not knowing what will happen next.
C Yes, and I will do anything to make it happen.

How do you feel about the power of magic?
A I respect and slightly fear it – we don't understand it and we shouldn't use something that we don't understand.
B I find it exciting and hope that great things can be achieved by using it.
C I want to control it so that I can use it to get what I want.

You disagree with a decision that your friend has made. What do you do?
A I speak to my friend and tell him why I think he is wrong.
B I say nothing and wait and see – he may know more than I do.
C I say nothing, but I enjoy it when I am proved right.

What do you think of chivalry?
A It is the height of honour and the code by which I would like to live my life.
B It is very admirable, but I'm not sure I'm brave enough to die for it!
C It is a weakness in those who follow it, and it can be exploited.

What comes first, power, people or possessions?
A Power
B People
C Possessions

When you are angry, how do you react?
A I shout and throw things!
B I cry and don't want to see anyone.
C I don't let anyone know how I feel, but I need to get my own back.

Your friend is in danger, but to save him you must risk your own life. What do you do?
A I don't even need to think about it – I will do everything I can to save him.
B I delay and try to find a safer way to save him.
C What is the point of both of us dying? I will grieve for my friend, but I will not risk my life to save him.

Mostly As
You have noble ideals and great ambitions. You are not embarrassed to be the centre of attention. You would fit in well as a knight of Camelot!

Mostly Bs
You are not interested in fame or glory. You care about people and you are not afraid to break with tradition. You would make a good sorcerer!

Mostly Cs
You are cunning and subtle, and you like to get your own way. You make a fearsome enemy. You should consider becoming an assassin for hire – there are lots of people who would like to replace Arthur on the throne!

In a small village miles from Camelot, a bedraggled young woman is mucking out a pigsty. It is a very ordinary scene, but this is no ordinary young woman. It is Gwen, and she is exhausted. Mucking-out is back-breaking work, but her heart is broken too. She has been exiled from her home and from the man she loves: Arthur.

Suddenly she hears screams. Southron soldiers are swarming into the village! They have come to round up the young men, and will slaughter anyone who stands in their way. The Southrons capture Gwen and take her to work as a slave for their leader, Helios.

Meanwhile, at Camelot, Arthur was making an announcement to his people. Camelot's claim to the lands of Gedref had been in dispute for a long time. Now the two kingdoms had reached an agreement. Part of that agreement was that Arthur would marry Princess Mithian. Everyone seemed pleased – except Merlin! He knew that Arthur still loved Gwen, but when he said so, Arthur grew angry.

"You ever say anything like that again, and I swear you'll join her in exile," he snapped. "Forever!"

Agravaine cornered Eoghan, the mapmaker's apprentice. He had ordered him to steal the plans.

The boy squirmed uneasily.

"I cannot do it," he said eventually.

"I cannot betray my master's trust."

"You'd rather betray mine?"

Agravaine snarled.

With one swift movement, he ended the boy's life.

When Agravaine told Morgana that he had failed to get the plans for her, she was angry and impatient. She told him to get them himself, no matter what the danger.

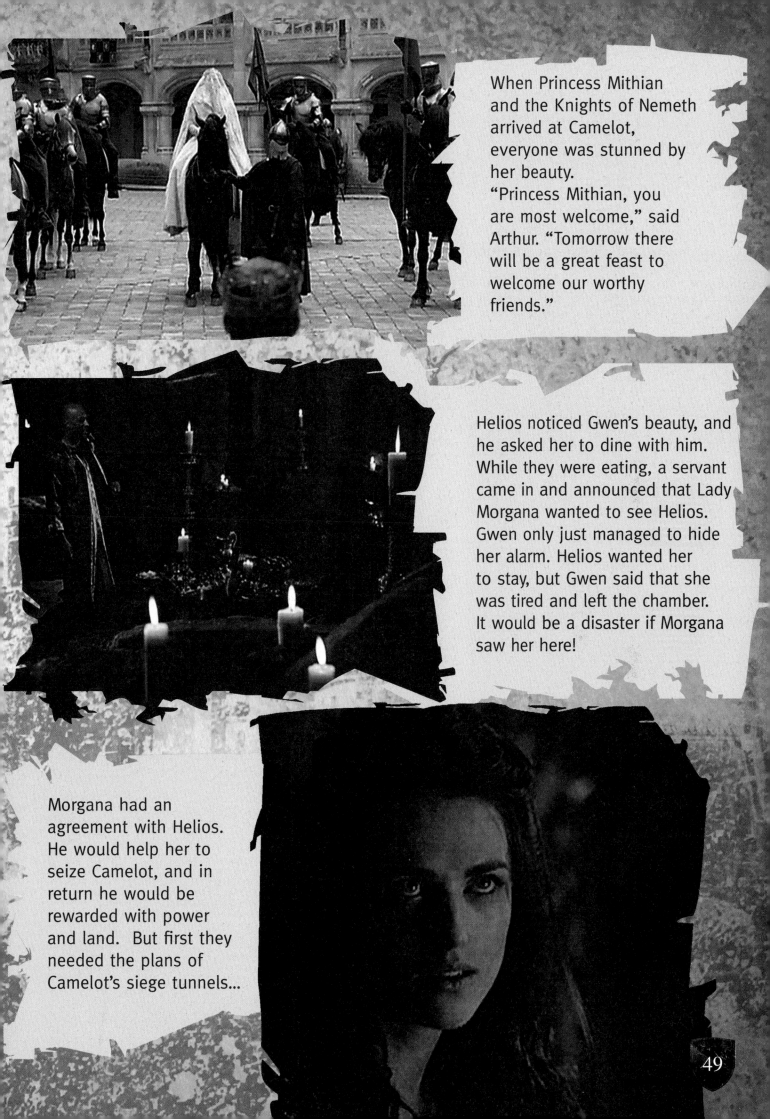

When Princess Mithian and the Knights of Nemeth arrived at Camelot, everyone was stunned by her beauty.
"Princess Mithian, you are most welcome," said Arthur. "Tomorrow there will be a great feast to welcome our worthy friends."

Helios noticed Gwen's beauty, and he asked her to dine with him. While they were eating, a servant came in and announced that Lady Morgana wanted to see Helios. Gwen only just managed to hide her alarm. Helios wanted her to stay, but Gwen said that she was tired and left the chamber. It would be a disaster if Morgana saw her here!

Morgana had an agreement with Helios. He would help her to seize Camelot, and in return he would be rewarded with power and land. But first they needed the plans of Camelot's siege tunnels...

Under the cover of darkness, Agravaine dragged Eoghan's body to the foot of a high wall, to make it look as if he fell. Then he slipped a letter into the boy's tunic.

When the body was found the next day, Agravaine suggested that they ask Gaius to look at the body.

When Gaius examined the body, he found the letter that Agravaine had planted.

"It's a letter from Odin's court," he said.

Agravaine read it and then hurried to find Arthur. The letter showed that Eoghan had been planning to sell the plans of the siege tunnels.

"It is possible the boy succeeded in his mission and was murdered for his pains," said Arthur. "We need to check the vaults."

Everything was going just as Agravaine had hoped. He and Arthur went to the mapmaker's room and they looked around at the scrolls that lined the walls.

"A complete inventory will be necessary, my lord," said Agravaine. "With your permission, I will start right away."

Arthur nodded, and Agravaine smiled. Nothing could stop him now.

That night, Agravaine delivered the plans of the siege tunnels to Morgana.

"As good as a key to the great gates," he said.

She used magic to make a copy of the plans, and then Agravaine returned to Camelot with the original scroll. It was time for the feast to welcome their visitors, and he could report that there were no plans missing.

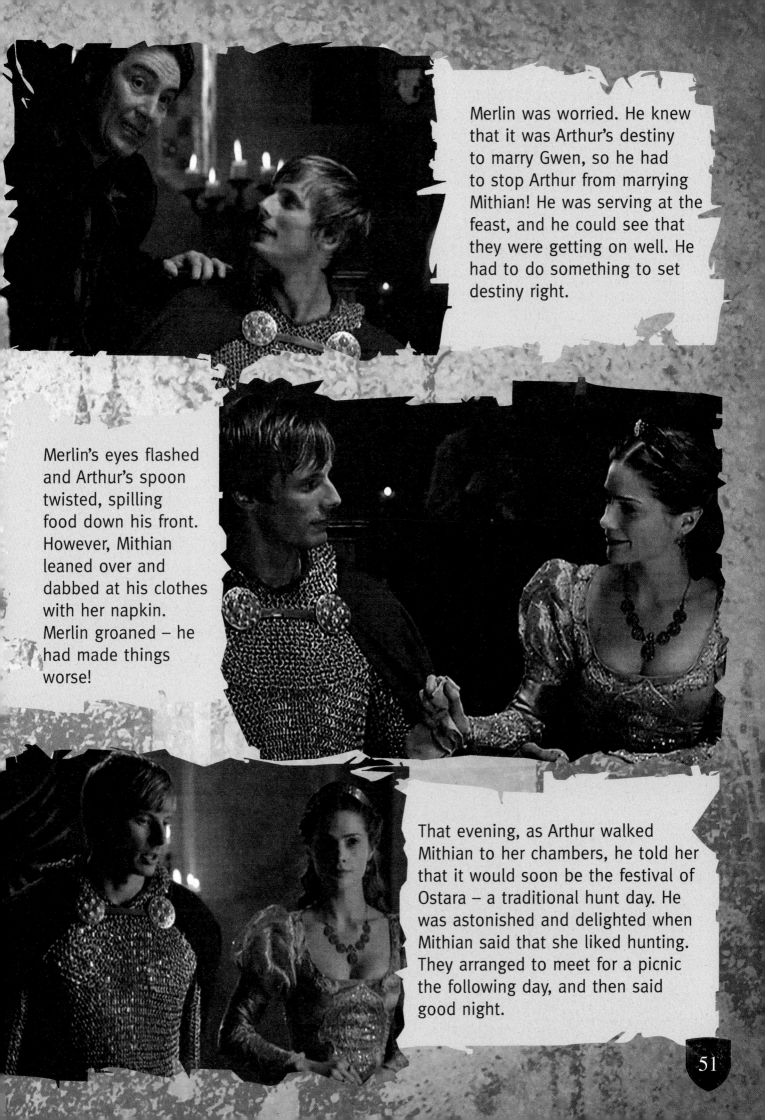

Merlin was worried. He knew that it was Arthur's destiny to marry Gwen, so he had to stop Arthur from marrying Mithian! He was serving at the feast, and he could see that they were getting on well. He had to do something to set destiny right.

Merlin's eyes flashed and Arthur's spoon twisted, spilling food down his front. However, Mithian leaned over and dabbed at his clothes with her napkin. Merlin groaned – he had made things worse!

That evening, as Arthur walked Mithian to her chambers, he told her that it would soon be the festival of Ostara – a traditional hunt day. He was astonished and delighted when Mithian said that she liked hunting. They arranged to meet for a picnic the following day, and then said good night.

Morgana gave the plans to Helios, who demanded to know where she had got them. "The King's uncle and most trusted advisor – Lord Agravaine," Morgana said. "I doubt you'll find a source more impeccable than that."

As they spoke, there was a sound in the shadows by the door. It was Gwen, and she had heard every word. She raced away into the darkness, but Helios glimpsed her leaving. He and Morgana searched her room, and Morgana recognised her dress. "Who was this woman?" she asked.

"A serving wench I recently acquired," said Helios. "Guinevere."

"She's no serving wench," said Morgana in a grim voice. "We must find her. Now." Morgana knew that Gwen would be making her way to Camelot . . . and to Arthur.

Gwen raced through the Darkling Woods, but she could hear the hoof beats of Morgana's horse thumping closer and closer. At last, exhausted and filthy, she was captured.

"Gwen, how nice to see you again," Morgana said.

Her voice was like the hiss of a snake.

"Leave me be," said Gwen. "You've already done enough harm."

Morgana's eyes flashed and Gwen was lifted off her feet and slammed into a tree. She slumped to the forest floor, unconscious.

Morgana tore a chain from around Gwen's neck. Upon the chain was a ring that Arthur had given her.

"You wish to see your beloved Arthur again," she said, "and so you shall."

Merlin was getting worried. Mithian was a spirited, attractive woman, and Arthur liked her. There seemed to be nothing Merlin could do to drive them apart.

During the hunt, Arthur and the other hunters were chasing a deer when Merlin caught sight of its reflection in a pool. With a terrible shock, he realised that it was Gwen! Morgana had enchanted her to look like a deer, hoping that she would be killed.

Arthur slid a bolt into his crossbow, took aim and fired . . .

Merlin's eyes flashed and the arrow missed. "I thought you were a good shot, my Lord," said Mithian, firing an arrow after the deer. "A gold sovereign says she's hit!"

The hunters tracked the deer deeper into the woods, until they reached a clearing. Sir Leon found deer tracks on the ground, but Arthur found something else – Gwen's ring.

Arthur mounted his horse. His good mood had disappeared completely. Suddenly, Gwen was all he could think about.

"There'll be no more sport today," he said.

That night, Merlin returned to the Darkling Woods and found Gwen lying on the ground, blood running from a wound in her side. "Ic haele thina throwunga," Merlin muttered. The blood stopped flowing and the wound healed. Gwen told Merlin about Agravaine's betrayal, and begged him to warn Arthur.

Arthur didn't believe that his uncle was against him. "The idea is preposterous," he said "I have known my uncle since I was a child. I refuse to believe that he would ever betray Camelot."

They checked the mapmaking room and found that the plans were still there. There was no way that Merlin could prove that Agravaine was a traitor.

Mithian was witty, intelligent and beautiful . . . but she wasn't Gwen.

"How can I love someone who betrayed me?" Arthur asked Merlin. "It doesn't make any sense. Yet how can I make myself love another? Tell me that."

"You must do what your heart tells you, Sire," said Merlin.

"What if I don't know what that is?" asked the King.

"I think you do," Merlin replied.

Arthur told Princess Mithian that he could not marry her. At first she was hurt and angry, but when he offered her all the disputed land of Gedref, her astonishment overcame her anger.

"You would give up your ancient claims?" she asked.

"I have no desire for war," he said. "Or to grieve you any more than I already have."

Mithian gazed at him thoughtfully.

"Tell me, who is it that trumps a princess?" she asked. "From what great family does she come?"

"None," said Arthur. "She is the daughter of a blacksmith."

Mithian was amazed.

"And for her you would risk your kingship, your kingdom?" she asked.

"Without her they are worth nothing to me," he replied.

Mithian saw the strength of his feelings, and knew that nothing could change his mind.

"I would have given my own kingdom to be so loved," she said in a low voice.

As she left, Merlin felt a mixture of relief and worry. Arthur was still free to marry Gwen and fulfill his destiny, but Merlin knew that dark times lay ahead.

CODE BREAKER

Merlin has found a list of those who will help Morgana to seize the throne, but he needs your help to read it.
Can you crack the code and read the names on the list?

1. ᚠᚷᚱᚨᚷᛁᚾM

2. ᛞᚨᛚᚢᚱᚨᛁᚾ

3. ᛗᚨᚱᚷᚨᚢᛋM

4. ᛋMᚾᚱMᛞ

5. ᚦᚢMMᚾ ᚠᚾᛏᛁᛋ

6. ᚺMᛏᛚᛁᛋ

7. ᚠᛁᛏᚢᚾᛋᚠ

8. ᛗᚨᚱᛞᚨᚱMᛞ

ᚠ ᚢ ᚦ ᚨ ᚱ ᛚ ᚷ ᚹ ᚾ ᛁ ᛃ ᛉ ᛈ ᛣ
f u q o r c g w h ▢ i j z p x

ᛏ ᛒ ᛖ ᛗ ᛙ ᛞ ᛝ ᚠ ᚻ ᛏ ᚥ ᛉ ᛋ
t b e m l ▢ œ æ y ǣ ▢ k s

VILLAINS GALLERY

Identify Camelot's enemies, and be on your guard against them!

ALATOR

Warrior, priest and sorcerer

BORDEN

Thief and sorcerer

DOCHRAID

Repulsive creature of the Old Religion

HELIOS

Greedy and unscrupulous warlord

LAMIA

Deadly shape-shifting serpent-girl

CEDRIC

Thief and fraudster

KING ODIN

A monarch of a kingdom beside a shore

QUEEN ANNIS

Ruler of Caerleon

ALVARR

Dangerous and violent sorcerer

THE GLEEMAN

The Gleeman, a circus master and an assassin

57

POTION PUZZLE

Gaius needs your help - he has sent Merlin all over the Kingdom to retrieve these rare ingredients but now has forgotten the order of which way they should be mixed.

1. -Nettle Rue Foxglove, Nettle Rue _____

2. -Juniper Juniper Mallow Juniper Juniper Monkshood, Juniper Juniper Mallow Juniper Juniper_____

It's very important to get the order of ingredients right.

Look carefully at the recipes. Can you figure out which missing ingredient goes with which potion from the list below?
Hemlock - Monkshood - Sage - Foxglove

4. –Hemlock Belladonna Hemlock Anise Anise, Hemlock Belladonna _____ Anise Anise

3. –Valerian Yarrow Yarrow Sage, Valerian Yarrow Yarrow ____

CHANGING TIMES

The Camelot knights have unearthed a haunting secret, but dark magic has muddled events and sent time into a spin. Draw on your own powers to put time right, and sort these images into the correct order of what happened next.

Write your answer here

THE SWORD IN THE STONE

PART 1

It is the Feast of Beltane, and Arthur is sitting at a festive table with his courtiers. Everyone is happy and enjoying themselves, but the seat at the far end of the table is empty. Agravaine is missing.

Outside Camelot, Agravaine lets assassins into Camelot. They spread pitch and tar down the street, and then Agravaine sets fire to it. Helios and Morgana watch as flames spread across the lower town.
"It's time," says Morgana.

Camelot is in complete panic. The fires are out of control, and crowds of people are trying to escape as the Southron army swarms through the flames towards them.

Gwaine, caked in sweat and soot, bursts in upon the feast.
"Sire, we are under attack," he gasps. "They are within the city walls…"
Arthur and his knights leap up. Camelot needs them!

As Arthur leads his knights into battle, the Southrons surge into the palace courtyard. Soon the council chambers are littered with the dead and the dying. "We can't hold them for much longer!" Sir Leon yells. "Retreat!"

The King fights on, but there are too many Southrons for even him to defeat. Merlin finds him staggering down a corridor, clutching his ribs in pain. At last Arthur knows the truth – Agravaine is a traitor.

Morgana reaches the throne room and gazes at the throne in triumph as the citadel burns. She controls Camelot – now she wants Arthur dead.

Gaius binds Arthur's broken ribs and the Knights of the Round Table gather around him. They know that their enemies are coming to kill Arthur. "We must get him to safety while we still can," says Sir Percival.

"Arthur will never abandon his people," says Sir Gwaine. "He'd rather die."

While the knights are barricading the doors, Merlin incants a spell to make the King lose his will, so they can persuade him to leave Camelot. Arthur blinks dreamily. "We need to leave now, Sire," Merlin says.

"Of course," says Arthur.

Sir Gwaine prepares to hold the Southron warriors off for as long as he can. Gaius bravely stays behind too, fearing that he will slow them down. When the Southrons burst into the chamber, Arthur has gone.

"Prepare the horses," says Morgana. "We're going on a hunt."

Merlin, Sir Percival and Sir Elyan escape with Arthur, and soon they are hurrying through the Darkling Woods.

"We have to make it across the border," says Sir Elyan. " We need to find sanctuary."

"I know a place," says Merlin. "Ealdor."

Just then they hear the sound of hooves drawing nearer. It is Morgana with Agravaine and his men. She glimpses the knights and sends a magical blast after them, flinging them into the trees.

Sir Percival is lost, and Sir Elyan stays behind to hold off the Southrons. Now there is just Merlin left, with a king who has lost his willpower.

"I think we're safe for now," says Merlin, "but we need to find you some kind of disguise."

"Whatever you say," Arthur replies politely. "I'm entirely in your hands."

Merlin takes some tatty old clothes from a line outside a woodsman's hut, and Arthur puts them on. They are much too small, but thanks to Merlin's spell, the King doesn't complain!

Morgana tortures Sir Elyan to find out where Arthur is hiding. Even Agravaine can hardly bear to hear his screams of agony. At last, in pain beyond all imagining, Sir Elyan reveals that Arthur is going to Ealdor. Morgana sends Agravaine to catch him.

In the Forest of Balor, Merlin and Arthur come across a small group of carts, guarded by heavily armed men. Merlin hides, but when he turns around he sees an incredibly beautiful woman pointing a sword at him.

The woman's name is Isolde, and she is a skilled warrior. She takes Merlin and Arthur to a handsome man called Tristan, who is leaning against a cart. They are smugglers, and agree to let Merlin and Arthur travel with them – for a fee.

Merlin tells Tristan and Isolde that Arthur is a simpleton. "Look after him, do you?" Tristan asks.

"Without me he wouldn't last a day," says Merlin with a grin.

They set up camp for the night, and in the morning Arthur is back to his normal self.
"You'd better have a damn good explanation for this, Merlin," he growls.
Merlin explains, and Arthur has to go along with it – although he isn't happy acting like a simpleton!

Tristan is suspicious about Arthur's sword. It is too good for a simpleton to have!
Merlin says that he won it in a card game.
"I hope for your sake that's true," says Tristan.
"I'd hate to think that I was riding with a Knight of Camelot."

Isolde bursts out laughing.
"A Knight of Camelot?" she exclaims. "Look at him!"
   "You're right," says Tristan. "The Knights may be stupid, but they're not that stupid."

Suddenly an arrow whistles past them and thuds into the side of the cart. The
Southrons have found them! Instantly, Arthur draws his sword.
"Head for those trees," he tells Tristan and Isolde. "We'll cover you."

The four of them escape into the woods. Tristan holds a knife to Arthur's chest.

"They weren't after the cargo," he says. "They were after you. Who the hell are you?"

"My name is Arthur Pendragon," says Arthur. Tristan's mouth falls open.

"I've lost everything I've worked for for some good for nothing King?" he asks.

Before they can argue further, the Southrons spot them. Arthur, Isolde and Tristan fight well, but his beloved Isolde is injured. Her wounds need urgent treatment.

Arthur and Merlin ask Tristan and Isolde to go with them to Ealdor.

"Very well," says Tristan. "But know this, Arthur Pendragon. I do this for her. You and your kind bring nothing but misery to this land."

In the dungeons of Camelot, Morgana visits Sir Gwaine, Sir Elyan and Gaius. They ask for food, and she says that Gwaine will have to fight for it.

To earn food for himself and his friends, Morgana makes Sir Gwaine fight a monstrous Southron. Sir Gwaine only has a small wooden sword, but his speed and skill overcome the lumbering brute.

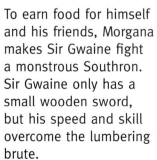

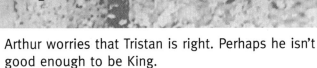

Arthur is devastated that Agravaine was a traitor all along.
"I feel like such a fool," he says. "I put such trust in him, and all this time I was blind to his treachery. As I was to Morgana's."
"You were deceived, Arthur," says Merlin. "It could happen to anyone."
"Yet it keeps on happening to me," replies Arthur sadly.

Arthur worries that Tristan is right. Perhaps he isn't good enough to be King.
"You are honest and brave and true-hearted," Merlin says. "And one day you will be the greatest King this land has ever known."

Next day, bedraggled and exhausted, the weary travellers arrive in Ealdor.
A woman rushes to Merlin and hugs him tight.
"Mother," he says with a smile.

Merlin cleans Isolde's wound and lets her rest.
"I'm sorry that I have brought this misfortune upon you," says Arthur.
"I still have my beloved Isolde," Tristan replies.
"Then you are richer than you know," Arthur murmurs.

Merlin glimpses Gwen through a crack in the hut wall.

"How's she been?" he asks.

"As well as can be expected," says his mother. "A broken heart takes time to mend."

That night, Arthur awakes from a dream to see Gwen sitting beside his bed. He gazes at her in astonishment, half wondering if he is still dreaming.

"I've missed you," she says.

"And I you," Arthur replies.

Her eyes are shining with love. He pulls her towards him and they hold each other as if they never want to let go.

Suddenly, screams shatter the peace of the night. Agravaine has found them! Southrons surround the village, carrying flaming torches.

Arthur, Merlin, Gwen, Tristan and Isolde escape, but Agravaine sees them racing into the woods.

"There!" he yells. "Get them!"

Turn to page 78 to find out what happened next!

SECRET SCROLL

Gaius has found a scroll that predicts the future, but it is damaged.
Can you help him by filling in the missing words?

Leon   sorceress   Dorocha   Merlin
Morgana   Lancelot   plans

1. Sir _____ is a brave and loyal knight of Camelot.

2. Morgause is a dangerous _____

3. The _____ must be stopped. The veil between the worlds has been torn open. Only Merlin can stop it.

4. No one must find out that _____ is the mysterious Emrys!

5. Agravaine is loyal to _____ He cannot be trusted.

6. Brave _____ has sacrificed his life, but he will rise again.

7. Morgana's _____ have been thwarted this time, but she grows more dangerous by the day.

GUESS WHO?

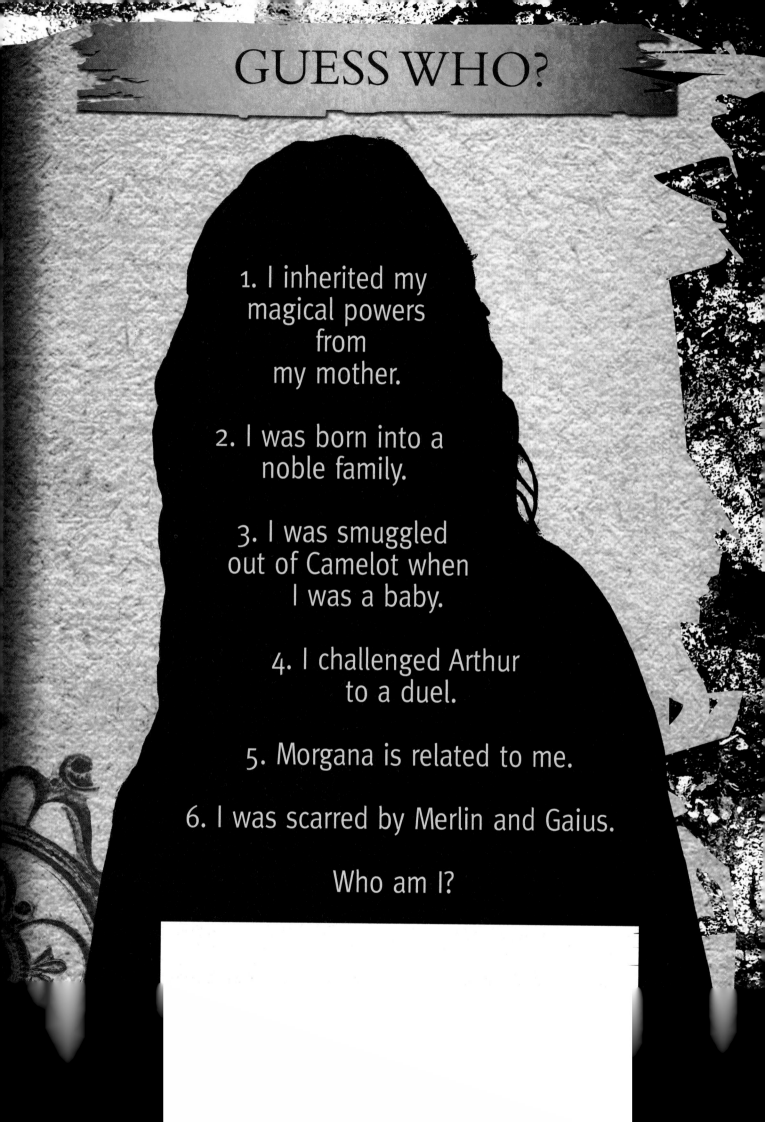

1. I inherited my magical powers from my mother.

2. I was born into a noble family.

3. I was smuggled out of Camelot when I was a baby.

4. I challenged Arthur to a duel.

5. Morgana is related to me.

6. I was scarred by Merlin and Gaius.

Who am I?

TRUE OR FALSE?

Look at these statements. Some of them are true but several are false. Can you pick fact from fiction?

Morgana is Uther's daughter.
True or Fales

Lancelot sacrifices his life to save Arthur.
True or Fales

Merlin is also known as Emrys.
True or Fales

Dragoon the Great is Merlin's grandfather.
True or Fales

Merlin opens the dragon egg by giving the dragon a name.
True or Fales

Agravaine is loyal to Morgana.
True or Fales

Lamia falls in love with Percival.
True or Fales

Gwen's real name is Guinevere.
True or Fales

WORDSEARCH

There are fifteen words hidden below. Can you find them? They may be written forwards, backwards, up, down or diagonally.

G	A	I	U	S	S	E	C	I	F	I	R	C	A	S
W	Q	W	C	Z	E	W	A	T	H	O	U	B	R	O
E	G	G	C	C	T	A	M	X	Z	L	H	M	T	R
N	K	Q	I	W	G	G	E	W	B	D	T	H	Q	C
T	K	G	E	K	A	J	L	R	K	S	R	A	X	E
F	A	K	Y	W	Y	N	O	M	K	B	A	F	P	R
M	E	R	D	G	U	U	T	K	M	P	V	O	P	E
J	A	K	Q	K	K	L	K	M	L	N	Z	D	A	R
M	E	R	L	I	N	H	F	S	A	Y	Q	I	F	G
O	Q	P	I	O	I	I	D	U	Y	E	Y	S	T	F
R	M	L	W	C	G	N	R	V	A	L	X	G	Z	G
G	X	L	N	G	H	R	A	4	R	Y	E	U	F	Q
A	Q	E	W	A	T	W	G	F	T	A	U	I	N	K
N	Y	P	P	F	S	F	O	L	E	H	B	S	W	G
A	S	S	A	S	S	I	N	Q	B	G	H	E	N	T

MERLIN	MAGIC	SACRIFICE
GAIUS	ARTHUR	GWEN
DRAGON	BETRAYAL	SPELL
ASSASSIN	MORGANA	DISGUISE
CAMELOT	KNIGHTS	ORCERER

73

HOW TO DRAW...

Use the grid below to study the mighty dragon, Kilgharrah. When your ready, use the grid opposite to try and copy the image.

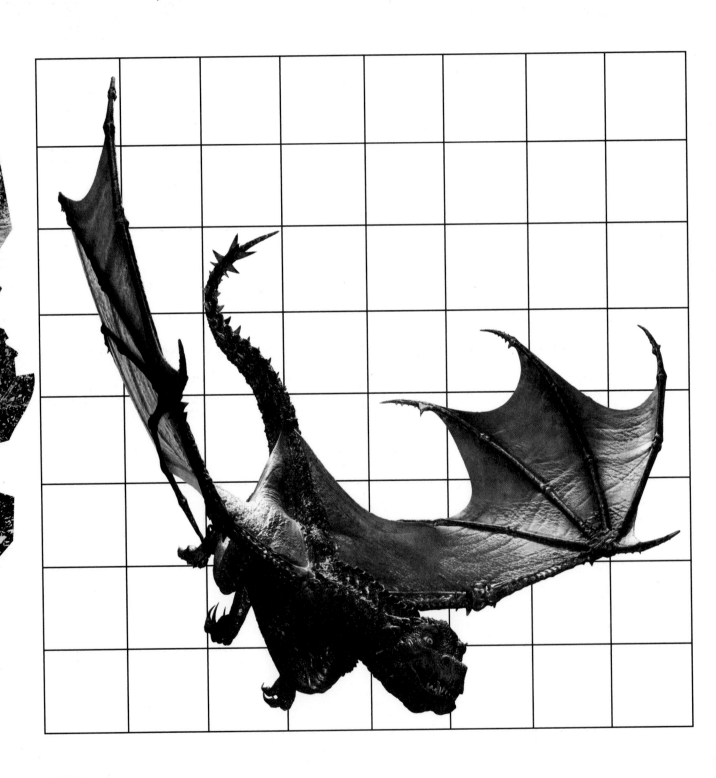

KILGHARRAH

Use all your new found skills and magic to help you draw The Mighty Dragon. We've drawn the top of his left wing to get you started...

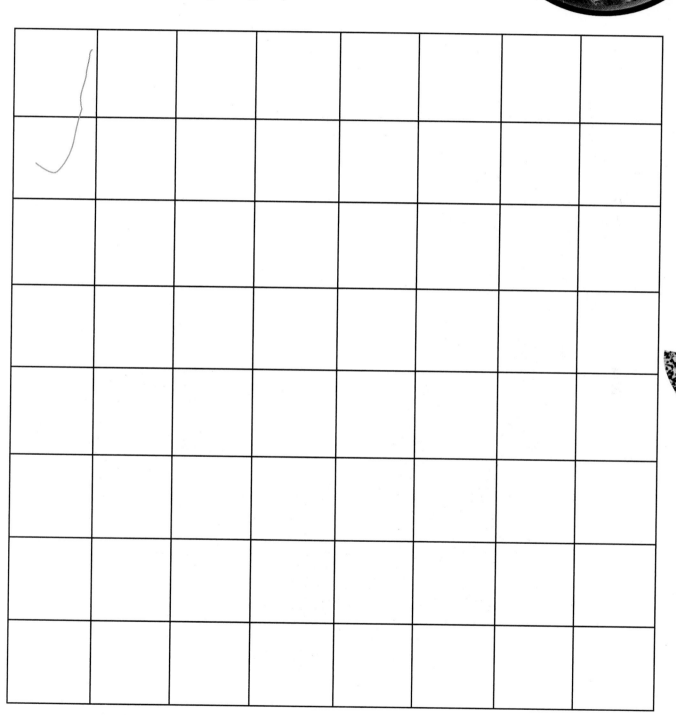

KNOW YOUR ENEMY!

Can you identify these suspicious characters? Look carefully at the pictures and write the names beneath.

1

2

3

4

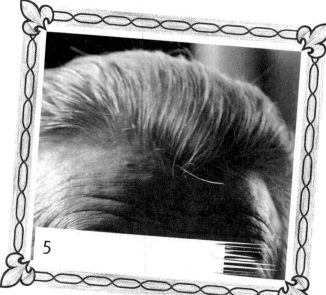

5

SECRET SUDOKU

Test your mental powers with this number game.
Every line, column and mini-grid must contain the numbers 1 to 9.

Apprentice Level

8	6	5					4	
4	1				7		9	8
	9		8	4			3	5
		2	1			8	6	9
1	7		6			3		
			3	9				2
					9	5	2	
		8	7					
5	4	6			1			

Master Level

4				5	8			
					7	4		9
5			4				7	8
	3				5	1		
8	6	5			3			
7				6			2	
		4		7			1	
	1					3	9	4
	8			9	4			

THE SWORD IN THE STONE

PART 2

Merlin, Arthur, Gwen, Tristan and the wounded Isolde tore through the woods. The ferocious Southrons were hard on their heels, but Merlin thought they would be safe in a maze of tunnels that he had played in as a child.

As they hurried into the tunnels, Merlin secretly called for help from the Great Dragon. The Southrons screamed and scattered as the mighty dragon hurtled out of the sky towards them. He unleashed a blast of fire and wheeled around to attack again.

Merlin led his friends through the tunnels, hoping that he could remember the way.
"So you know Arthur?" Tristan asked Gwen.
   "I was a servant in Camelot," she replied.
"So why are you here?"
   "He's my King," she said simply.
"Can't say I've detected many kingly qualities so far," Tristan grumbled.

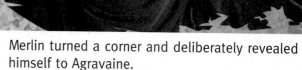

Suddenly they heard a noise. Agravaine and his men had managed to get into the tunnels!

"I'll go back," said Merlin. "I know these tunnels, Agravaine doesn't. You keep going."

He handed Arthur his torch.

"Merlin, don't do anything stupid," said Arthur.

They exchanged a smile, and then Merlin turned back and disappeared down the tunnel.

Merlin turned a corner and deliberately revealed himself to Agravaine.

"Merlin!" Agravaine exclaimed. "Where's Arthur? Tell me now – or I'll have to kill you."

"I don't think so," said Merlin.

He conjured a magical shockwave, sending Agravaine and his men crashing into the rocks. Agravaine hauled himself painfully to his feet.

"So it's you," he said in astonishment. "You're Emrys."

"That is what the druids call me," said Merlin.

Agravaine whipped a dagger from his belt and launched himself at Merlin. But the young warlock's eyes flashed, and Agravaine went flying into the rocks with a sickening crack. He lay dead.

Further along the tunnel, Arthur was getting worried. Where was Merlin?

"I'm going back," he said.

"For a servant?" Tristan asked incredulously.

Arthur headed back along the tunnel and Gwen looked at Tristan.

"You're wrong about him," she said.

Arthur found Merlin and they rejoined the others. After a long and tiring night, the weary travellers emerged from the tunnels and looked up at the mountains ahead of them. Arthur wanted to carry on, but Merlin thought differently.

"We must travel back towards Camelot," he said.

"No, we need to keep going," Arthur insisted.

"If we hole up in the Forest of Ascetir we'll

be safe, at least for a while," said Merlin.

"No," Arthur said again.

"If anyone's survived the battle that's where they'll be hiding," Merlin went on. Arthur suddenly felt very alone. He didn't know if he could trust his own decisions any more.

"All right," he said at last. "The Forest of Ascetir it is."

They set up camp for the night. While Gwen looked after the injured Isolde, Arthur and Tristan collected wood.

"First you go back to rescue your servant, now you're getting your hands dirty," said Tristan in a mocking voice. "But then again, why shouldn't you? You're just like everyone else. There's nothing special about you."

"Maybe you're right," said Arthur. "Maybe I don't deserve to be King."

"Well, that's all right, because you're not," said Tristan. "Not any more."

Arthur turned and walked away. Gwen tried to comfort him, but he told her to leave him alone. He still couldn't forgive her for what she had done to him.

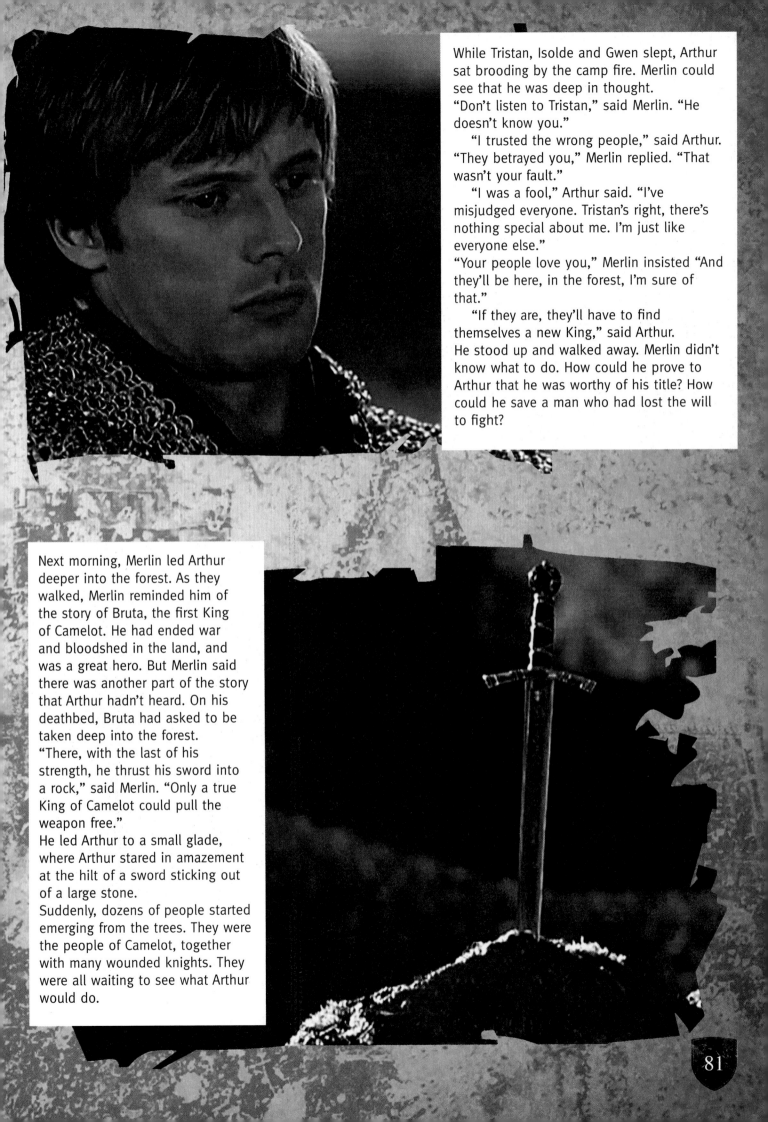

While Tristan, Isolde and Gwen slept, Arthur sat brooding by the camp fire. Merlin could see that he was deep in thought.

"Don't listen to Tristan," said Merlin. "He doesn't know you."

"I trusted the wrong people," said Arthur. "They betrayed you," Merlin replied. "That wasn't your fault."

"I was a fool," Arthur said. "I've misjudged everyone. Tristan's right, there's nothing special about me. I'm just like everyone else."

"Your people love you," Merlin insisted "And they'll be here, in the forest, I'm sure of that."

"If they are, they'll have to find themselves a new King," said Arthur. He stood up and walked away. Merlin didn't know what to do. How could he prove to Arthur that he was worthy of his title? How could he save a man who had lost the will to fight?

Next morning, Merlin led Arthur deeper into the forest. As they walked, Merlin reminded him of the story of Bruta, the first King of Camelot. He had ended war and bloodshed in the land, and was a great hero. But Merlin said there was another part of the story that Arthur hadn't heard. On his deathbed, Bruta had asked to be taken deep into the forest. "There, with the last of his strength, he thrust his sword into a rock," said Merlin. "Only a true King of Camelot could pull the weapon free."

He led Arthur to a small glade, where Arthur stared in amazement at the hilt of a sword sticking out of a large stone.

Suddenly, dozens of people started emerging from the trees. They were the people of Camelot, together with many wounded knights. They were all waiting to see what Arthur would do.

Arthur knew what he had to do – he just didn't believe he could do it. However, with everyone watching, he couldn't refuse. He reached down with both hands, took hold of the shining hilt and pulled, but nothing happened. He tried again, but the sword was locked tight inside the stone.

"You have to believe, Arthur," Merlin whispered. "You are destined to be Albion's greatest king. Nothing, not even this stone can stand in your way."

Arthur closed his eyes, put one hand around the hilt and pulled. Merlin's eyes flashed a deep gold, and then Arthur pulled out the sword with one fluid movement. A cheer went up and echoed around the glade.

"Long Live the King! Long Live the King!"

With his self-belief restored, Arthur started to plan the recapture of Camelot. Everyone was willing to fight for him. Even Tristan and Isolde were beginning to understand how special he was.

"You have shown us that you fight for what is right and fair," said Isolde. "And for that reason we would like to fight at your side."

"I would be honoured to have you at my side," said Arthur. "We stand together as equals."

Arthur was worried that they had no way to fight Morgana's magical powers. He didn't know that his trusted servant was more than a match for her. In the dead of night, Merlin returned to Camelot in his disguise as an old man. He enchanted a small corn doll and hung it under Morgana's bed...

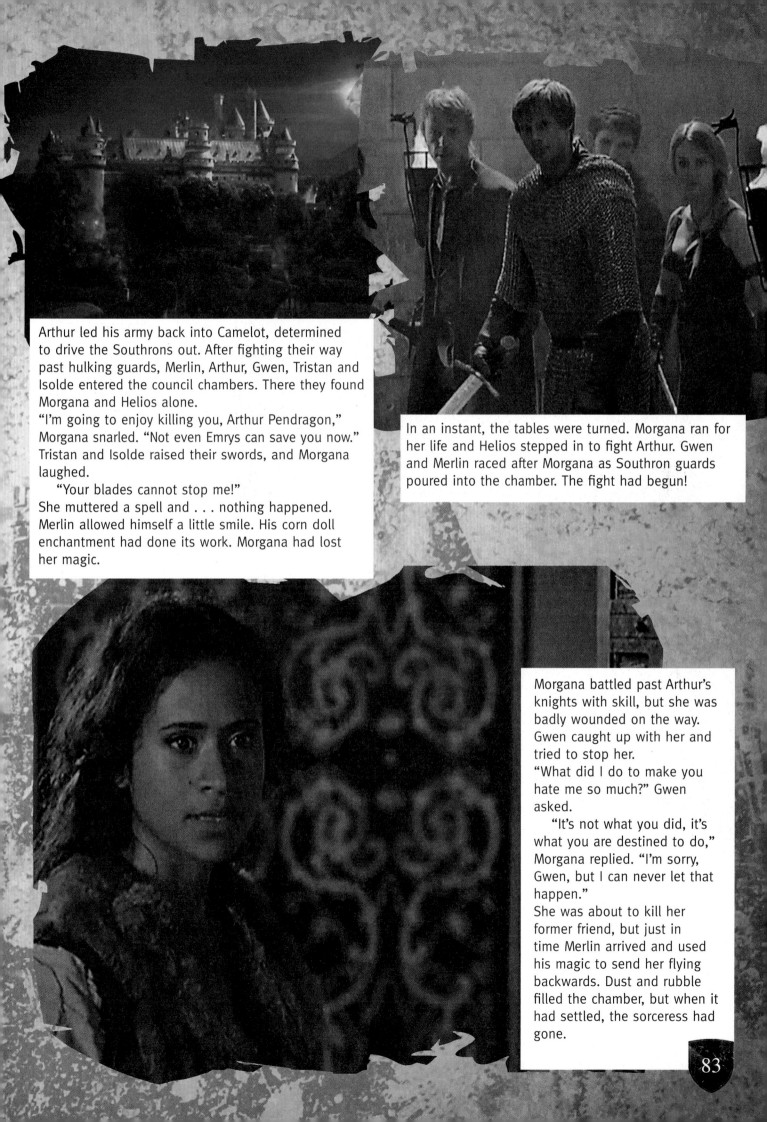

Arthur led his army back into Camelot, determined to drive the Southrons out. After fighting their way past hulking guards, Merlin, Arthur, Gwen, Tristan and Isolde entered the council chambers. There they found Morgana and Helios alone.

"I'm going to enjoy killing you, Arthur Pendragon," Morgana snarled. "Not even Emrys can save you now." Tristan and Isolde raised their swords, and Morgana laughed.

"Your blades cannot stop me!"

She muttered a spell and . . . nothing happened. Merlin allowed himself a little smile. His corn doll enchantment had done its work. Morgana had lost her magic.

In an instant, the tables were turned. Morgana ran for her life and Helios stepped in to fight Arthur. Gwen and Merlin raced after Morgana as Southron guards poured into the chamber. The fight had begun!

Morgana battled past Arthur's knights with skill, but she was badly wounded on the way. Gwen caught up with her and tried to stop her.

"What did I do to make you hate me so much?" Gwen asked.

"It's not what you did, it's what you are destined to do," Morgana replied. "I'm sorry, Gwen, but I can never let that happen."

She was about to kill her former friend, but just in time Merlin arrived and used his magic to send her flying backwards. Dust and rubble filled the chamber, but when it had settled, the sorceress had gone.

83

Meanwhile, Arthur was struggling to defend himself against Helios. The blows rained down on him, and he dropped his sword. All hope seemed lost . . . and then brave Isolde ran her sword through the warrior's chest. With his last breath of life, Helios turned and slashed at his killer, bringing her to her knees. Arthur was safe, but it had cost Isolde her life.

When Merlin and Gwen returned to the council chambers, they found Isolde dying in Tristan's arms.
"I'm sorry," she whispered. "Our dreams..."
    "Isolde, don't," he said, tears in his eyes.
"Hold me," she murmured.
He held her tight as her eyes closed for the last time. Arthur and Gwen gazed at each other, horrified by the utter waste of love before them.

As the sun rose over Camelot, and the long job of cleaning up began, Arthur found Gwen and took her hand.
"I want you to stay," he said. "Whatever happened between us... I don't care. I just don't ever want to lose you. Will you marry me?"
Gwen's eyes filled with happiness.
    "Yes," she said. "Yes, with all my heart!"

The wedding of Arthur and Guinevere was a day of joy that no one would ever forget. Merlin watched in delight as Arthur placed a crown on Gwen's head.
"By the sacred laws vested in me, I crown you Guinevere, Queen of Camelot," he said. "Long live the Queen!"
"Long live the Queen!" cheered the crowd.
"Long live the Queen!"

In the Forest of Ascetir, Morgana was dying, and she knew it. Blood poured from the wound in her side, and she closed her eyes, accepting her fate. Then a shadow crossed her face. It was Aithusa, the tiny dragon who Merlin had saved from Askhanar. It watched Morgana carefully, and then opened its mouth and breathed over her. Morgana blinked, and energy surged through her broken body once again.

For some unknown reason, the little dragon had saved her life...

MAGICAL MAZE

The last remaining dragon's egg is hidden in the tomb of Askhanar.
Help Merlin to find the egg and avoid running into Julius Borden.

DRAGON WISDOM

Everyone can learn something from the Great Dragon, Kilgharrah.
He is over a thousand years old, and his experience makes him a
staunch ally and a dangerous enemy.
Read his wise words and commit them to memory forever.

No young man, no matter how great, can know his destiny.

A half cannot truly hate that which makes it whole.

Trust the elements that are at your command.

How old a man can become… and yet change so little.

The dead do not return without reason.

What is made cannot be unmade.

The Old Religion is the magic of the earth itself. It is the essence which
binds all things together. It will last long beyond the time of men.

I've lived more than a thousand years, seen civilizations rise and fall. Do not
believe that you can lie to me.

It is the greatest force of all – love.

Trust is a double-edged sword.

To change the future is no simple matter.

A Dragonlord should never abuse their power.

All great struggles demand sacrifice.

GAIUS'S QUIZ PART TWO

Gaius is looking for a new apprentice. He needs someone with sharp observation skills and a good memory. Test your skills by answering the questions about series two below. You will have to think back a long way to get these questions right!

1. Who does Uther see in the well when he is going mad?

2. What is the name of Morgana's half sister?

3. Who accidently releases a goblin which possesses Gaius?

4. Which stranger helps Arthur and Merlin in a tavern brawl and becomes a Knight of the Round Table?

5. Who is Morgana's real father?

6. Which knight does Morgana bring back from the dead?

7. What relation is Agravaine to Arthur?

8. Who pulls the sword, Excalibur, from the stone?

9. Who is crowned Queen of Camelot?

10. What creature heals Morgana?

Now check your answers and add up your score with part one of Gaius's quiz.

LURKING IN THE SHADOWS

A dangerous enemy is hidden within this crossword.
Solve the clues and then rearrange the letters in the
shaded boxes to discover the villain.

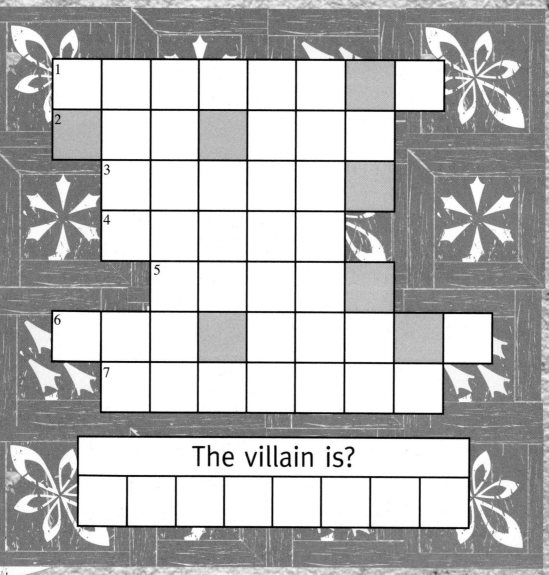

The villain is?

1. A commoner who longed to become a knight.
2. The greatest threat to Camelot, and Merlin's ultimate enemy.
3. Merlin's _____ arranged for him to stay with Gaius in Camelot.
4. Who outlawed magic?
5. Merlin's druidic name.
6. An enchanted sword.
7. A druid boy who became close to Morgana.

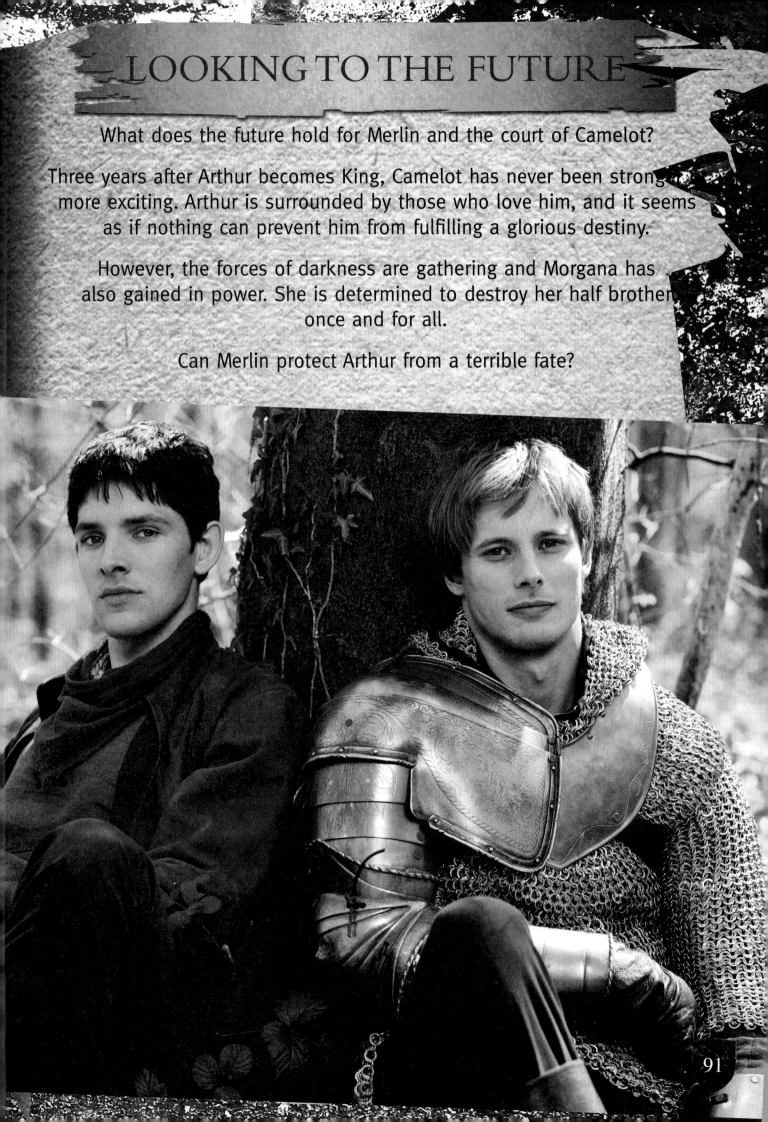

LOOKING TO THE FUTURE

What does the future hold for Merlin and the court of Camelot?

Three years after Arthur becomes King, Camelot has never been stronger, more exciting. Arthur is surrounded by those who love him, and it seems as if nothing can prevent him from fulfilling a glorious destiny.

However, the forces of darkness are gathering and Morgana has also gained in power. She is determined to destroy her half brother once and for all.

Can Merlin protect Arthur from a terrible fate?

ANSWERS

Pages 26-27. Gaius's Quiz Part One
1. Cedric
2. Kilgharrah
3. Morgana
4. Morgana
5. Lancelot
6. She is a troll
7. Aredian
8. A magic bracelet
9. She turns into a ferocious Bastet
10. A love potion

Page 28. Crossword

Page 31. Who Said That?
1. Julius Borden
2. Agravaine
3. Morgana
4. Merlin
5. Gaius
6. Arthur
7. Lancelot
8. The Great Dragon

Page 42. Word Scamble
1. THE GLEEMAN
2. JULIUS BORDEN
3. AGRAVAINE
4. LAMIA
5. MORGANA
6. DOCHRAID
7. THE DOROCHA
8. ODIN

Page 44. Crossword Challengw

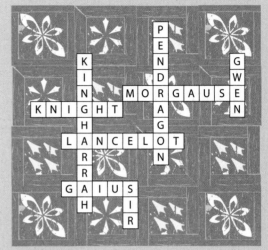

Page 56. Code breaker
1. Agravaine   5. Queen Annis
2. Dochraid   6. Helios
3. Morgause   7. Aithusa
4. Cenred   8. Mordred

Missing Letters:

†n ⋈d ᚠa ᚷv

Page 58-59. Potion Puzzle
1. Foxglove   3. Sage
2. Monkshood   4. Hemlock

Page 60-61. Changing Times
4, 6, 9, 12, 11, 1, 7, 3, 5, 10, 8, 2,

Page 70. Secret Scroll
1. Leon   5. Morgana
2. sorceress   6. Lancelot
3. Dorocha   7. plans
4. Merlin

Pages 71. Guess Who?
Morgause

Page 72. True or False
1. True   5. True
2. True   6. True
3. True   7. False
4. False   8. True

Page 73. Wordsearch

G	A	I	U	S	S	E	C	I	F	I	R	C	A	S
W	Q	W	C	Z	E	W	A	T	H	O	U	B	R	O
E	G	G	C	C	T	A	M	X	Z	L	H	M	T	R
N	K	Q	I	W	G	G	E	W	B	D	T	H	Q	C
T	K	G	E	K	A	J	L	R	K	S	R	A	X	E
F	A	K	Y	W	Y	N	O	M	K	B	A	F	P	R
M	E	R	D	G	U	U	T	K	M	P	V	O	P	E
J	A	K	Q	K	K	L	K	M	L	N	Z	D	A	R
M	E	R	L	I	N	H	F	S	A	Y	Q	I	F	G
O	Q	P	I	O	I	I	D	U	Y	E	Y	S	T	F
R	M	L	W	C	G	N	R	V	A	L	X	G	Z	G
G	X	L	N	G	H	R	A	4	R	Y	E	U	F	Q
A	Q	E	W	A	T	W	G	F	T	A	U	I	N	K
N	Y	P	P	F	S	F	O	L	E	H	B	S	W	G
A	S	S	A	S	S	I	N	Q	B	G	H	E	N	T

Page 76. Know Your Enemy

1. Morgana
2. Agravaine
3. Odin
4. Lamia
5. The Gleeman

Page 77. Secret Sudoku

8	6	5	9	3	2	7	4	1
4	1	3	5	6	7	2	9	8
2	9	7	8	4	1	6	3	5
3	5	2	1	7	4	8	6	9
1	7	9	6	2	8	3	5	4
6	8	4	3	9	5	1	7	2
7	3	1	4	8	9	5	2	6
9	2	8	7	5	6	4	1	3
5	4	6	2	1	3	9	8	7

4	7	6	9	5	8	2	3	1
1	2	8	6	3	7	4	5	9
5	9	3	4	2	1	6	7	8
2	3	9	7	4	5	1	8	6
8	6	5	2	1	3	9	4	7
7	4	1	8	6	9	5	2	3
9	5	4	3	7	6	8	1	2
6	1	7	5	8	2	3	9	4
3	8	2	1	9	4	7	5	5

Page 86. Magical Maze

Pages 88-89. Gaius's Quiz Part One

1. His dead wife, Ygraine
2. Morgause
3. Merlin
4. Gwaine
5. Uther
6. Lancelot
7. His Uncle
8. Arthur
9. Gwen
10. Aithusa, the white dragon

Page 90. Secret Sudoku

L	A	N	C	E	L	O	T
M	O	R	G	A	N	A
M	O	T	H	E	R
U	T	H	E	R
E	M	R	Y	S
E	X	C	A	L	I	B	U	R
M	O	R	D	R	E	D

| M | O | R | G | A | U | S | E |